MAGICAL

STORIES FROM

INDIAN MYTHOLOGY

Magical Stories From Indian Mythology

ISBN : 978-93-5049-432-5

Reprinted in 2012

Published by :

SHREE BOOK CENTRE
8, Kakad Indl Estate, S. Keer Marg, Matunga West,
Mumbai - 400016, INDIA.
Phone : 91-22-24377516 / 24374559
Telefax : 91-22-24309183
E-mail : sales@shreebookcentre.com

Printed in India

Preface

Indian mythology is replete with stories of gods, goddesses, divine nymphs, worthy kings, virtuous queens, tyrannical rulers and brave lieutenants. The stories talk about divine feats, treachery, bravery, sacrifice, love and devotion.

Popular stories from Indian Mythology have been compiled in this book. To make reading easy for your child, simple language has been used in large print. The colourful illustrations will ensure that your child will enjoy reading the book from start to finish. The glossary of difficult words and their meanings at the end of each book will enhance your child's vocabulary.

Lead your child into the fascinating world of Indian mythology! The journey will be delightful!

CONTENTS

1. Krishna and Kaliya   1

2. Bheema Meets Hanuman   13

3. Satyavan and Savitri   25

4. Prahlada   37

5. Shiva and Sati   49

6. The Pandavas' Journey to Heaven   61

Krishna and Kaliya

Krishna and Kaliya

On the banks of the River Yamuna, there once was a beautiful village named Gokul. Lord Krishna, as a child, lived there with his foster parents, Nanda and Yashoda. Everyone in Gokul adored Krishna. He was very intelligent and brave.

Krishna and his friends would often go playing near the river. They would climb up the trees and run around the rocks. Life in Gokul was quite peaceful, until one day, a many-headed serpent named Kaliya made his way into the river.

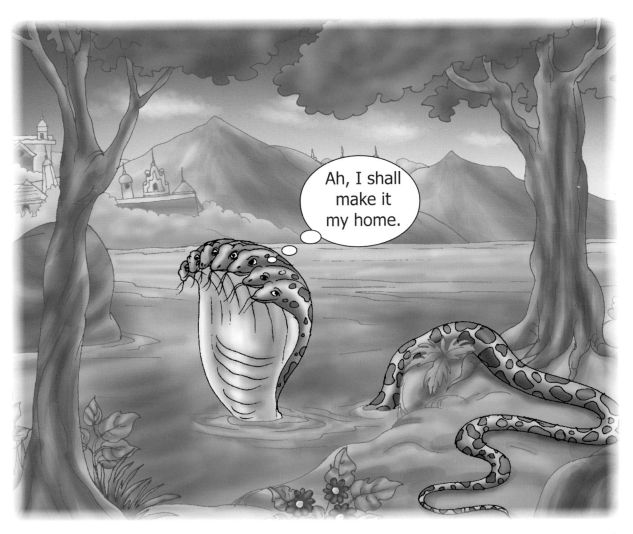

He began to live there and spread his venom in the water. Just a drop of his venom could kill. So far, the river had been the main source of water for the people of Gokul. But now, Kaliya had polluted it.

Life in Gokul became extremely difficult without water, but no one dared to drive Kaliya away from there. People feared even to go near the river, let alone use its water. Mothers were extra careful not to let their children wander that side.

5

But one day, little Krishna and his friends went to play near the Yamuna. "Ah, our favourite spot!" they sighed with joy. They began to play with a ball. Suddenly, the ball slipped from a boy's hand and went bouncing into the river.

6

Krishna's friends were frightened. But Krishna was not. "Don't worry, friends!" he said, "I will get the ball from the river."

"NO!" cried the boys, "Kaliya lives there!"

"So what?" said Krishna, "He cannot stop me from entering the river. Nothing will happen to me!"

Krishna dived into the river. His friends were terribly frightened. They ran to Nanda and told him all that had happened. Meanwhile, Krishna reached the bottom of the river where Kaliya was resting. He found the ball.

Suddenly, Kaliya opened his eyes and hissed, "Who is there?"

Krishna stood boldly in front of Kaliya.

"How dare you come here?" Kaliya fumed, "Don't you know this river is mine?"

"No, you have just taken it by force," said Krishna, "and that is not right!"

"So, you will tell me what is right and what is not?" hissed Kaliya, raising his hood in anger, threatening Krishna.

But Krishna swiftly turned around and jumped on to Kaliya's head. Thumping his tiny feet on the hood, he then began to dance!

Kaliya writhed in pain, as he felt each step of Krishna fall like a giant rock crushing his head. Soon, the mighty snake could not bear it anymore.

"Spare me please," Kaliya begged. "Only if you leave this place forever," said Krishna. Kaliya promised to do so. Krishna then stopped his dance.

As Krishna emerged from the river, standing upon Kaliya's hood, holding the ball, people were filled with awe. Kaliya asked for their forgiveness and left the place forever. The river was once again fresh and pure. The villagers thanked and praised Krishna.

Bheema meets Hanuman

Bheema Meets Hanuman

He will have the strength of a thousand elephants.

Bheema was the second of the Pandava brothers, the five righteous princes, who fought the great Mahabharata war against their evil cousins, the Kauravas. The Pandavas were sons of Pandu, but born through the blessings of gods. Bheema, the strongest, was born of Vayu, the God of Wind.

As he grew up in the kingdom of Hastinapur, Bheema was trained in warfare and martial arts. The mace was his favourite weapon and there was no one who could defeat him at that. Bheema performed many heroic exploits. But, gradually he became very vain and overconfident.

Once, it so happened that the Pandavas were defeated in a game of dice with the Kauravas, and were exiled from Hastinapur. The five brothers, along with their wife Draupadi, left their palace and began to live in a small hut in the Himalayan forests.

One day, sitting outside her hut, Draupadi saw a strange and beautiful flower falling from the air. It had the sweetest fragrance. Draupadi picked up the flower and went to Bheema. "Please get me some more of these flowers," she requested.

Bheema knew that the flower in question grew only in a remote part of the forest and that it was very difficult to reach up there. But he did not want to disappoint his wife. So, he picked up his mace and started on the narrow, winding path.

There were rocks and bushes on either side. Bheema walked fast but carefully. When he reached the dense part of the forest, the path became even narrower.

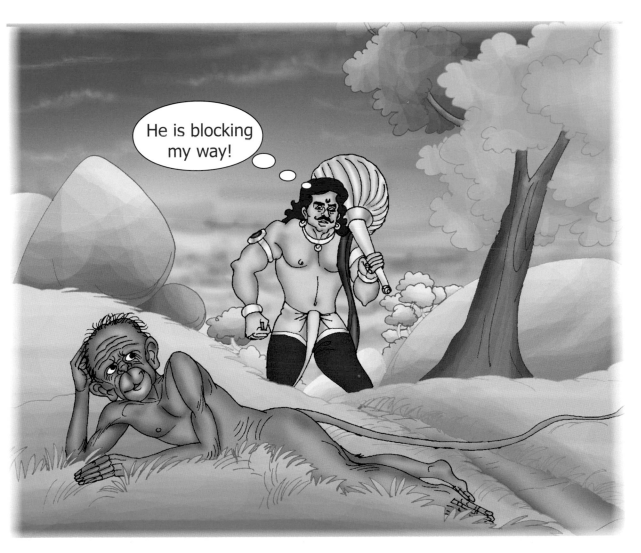

Suddenly, Bheema saw a monkey lying across the path. He snapped his fingers and shouted at the monkey, "Hey, move aside!" But the monkey did not budge.

"Can't you hear me, you foolish monkey?" Bheema cried, "You are blocking my way!" The monkey still did not move. Bheema was enraged.

"Will you move aside or shall I throw you out of my way?" he roared. At this, the monkey said, "O brother! As you can see, I am old and weak, unable to move myself. Why don't you lift me and place me aside?"

"Well, I think that is what I must do!" Bheema said haughtily.

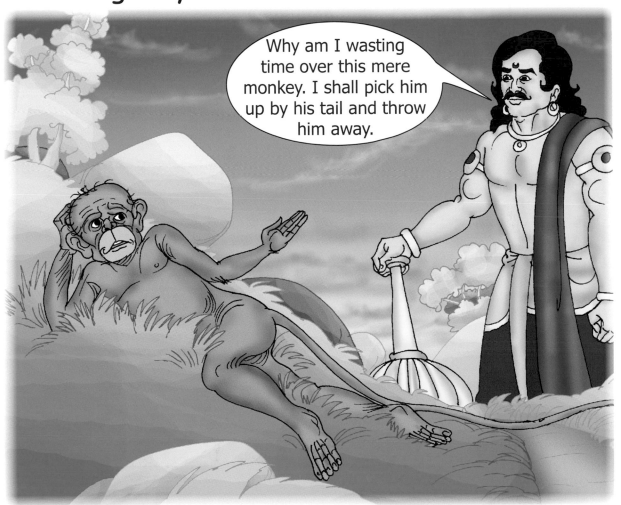

He grabbed the monkey's tail and tried to lift it. But it seemed to be very heavy. Bheema applied all his strength, but to his shock and surprise, he was not even able to shake the tail, let alone lift it!

Bheema's vanity received a big blow. He tried again and again, but failed to make the monkey budge.

"Please tell me who you are," Bheema asked, finally.

"Didn't you hear me call you 'Brother'?" smiled the monkey, "I am Hanuman. Like you, I too was born of Vayu, the Wind-God."

Bheema fell at Hanuman's feet, asking for his forgiveness. He had realised his mistake in being so vain.

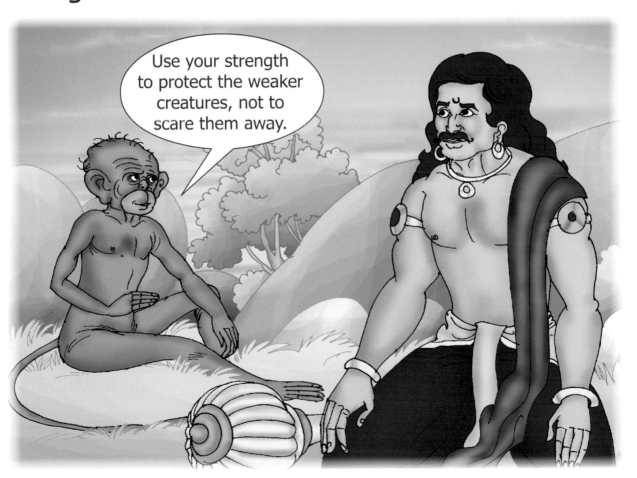

Hanuman then swelled up his body to massive proportions. Bheema was humbled before that huge cosmic form. He vowed never to misuse his might again. Taking blessings from Hanuman, Bheema went on his way.

He found the flowers that Draupadi wanted, and went back home. In time, he used his strength to fight the war of Mahabharata.

Satyavan and Savitri

Satyavan and Savitri

Once, King Ashvapati ruled the kingdom of Madra. He had all the comforts and luxuries a king would enjoy. Still he longed for something, and that was an heir. For, he was childless.

He began to worship Sun-God Savitir, performing severe penance for many years.

At last, pleased by his devotion and faith, Savitir appeared before him. "Ask what you want!" he commanded.

"Bless me with a son, O Lord!" replied Ashvapati, with tears in his eyes.

I want an heir to my throne!

Savitir blessed him with a daughter. "But she will be equal to many sons," he added.

Soon, his words came true and the queen gave birth to a lovely daughter. King Ashvapati's joy knew no bounds. He named the girl Savitri.

Savitri grew up to be a very intelligent and brave young girl. One day, her father asked her, "I want to fix your marriage. Do you have anyone in mind?"

"I have given my heart to Satyavan, O father," she replied.

Ashvapati consulted the great Sage Narada. "Oh, it is a wrong choice!" said the Sage, "Satyavan is the son of a blind king, Dyumatsena, who has lost his kingdom to an enemy, and is living in a forest. Moreover, Satyavan is destined to die – that too, in just a year!"

Ashvapati tried to dissuade Savitri, but she was firm in her decision to marry Satyavan. Finally, Ashvapati gave in and approached Dyumatsena in the forest. Both the families agreed and Savitri and Satyavan were married.

After that, Savitri accompanied Satyavan into the forest. Days and months passed. Soon the day came on which Satyavan was to die. Savitri and Satyavan had gone into the forest to gather wood. Right at the stipulated time, Satyavan fell unconscious. Savitri sat comforting him, placing his head on her lap.

Suddenly, there appeared Yama, the God of Death. He had arrived to take Satyavan away.
"I too want to come with you, O lord!" said Savitri.
"That is not possible!" said Yama.
"How will I live without my husband, O lord?" asked Savitri.

As Yama carried Satyavan away, Savitri followed him. Yama asked her to stay back, but she would not listen.

"Do not be so cruel to me, O Yama! Let me come with my husband. Or return him to me," she said.

Yama was impressed by her devotion and love. He offered her boons – anything, except for the life of Satyavan! "Ask for anything but your husband's life!" he said.

First, Savitri asked for the boon of eyesight for her father-in-law. Next, she asked for her father-in-law's kingdom to be returned to him. Third, she asked for a hundred sons to be born to her father. And lastly, she said, "I wish to have a hundred sons!"

So be it!

Now Savitri could not have a hundred sons without her husband! So, to be true to his word, Yama had to return Satyavan's life to him. Thus, a devoted and steadfast wife outwitted Yama and brought her husband back to life. Savitri and Satyavan lived on happily for many years.

Prahlada

Prahlada

Death shall come to you neither by man nor beast, neither during the day nor the night; neither in the house nor outside; neither on the earth nor in the sky; and no weapon can harm you.

Once, there lived an ardent devotee of Lord Vishnu, named Prahlada. His father, the demon-king Hiranyakashipu, was a tyrant. He was against the worship of Lord Vishnu, and wished himself to be worshipped as the lord of the universe. So, he pleased Brahma by his penance and attained a special boon. According to it, Hiranyakashipu could not be killed by any weapon, neither in his palace nor outside of it, neither in the day nor in the night, neither on the ground nor in the sky, and not by any human being or animal!

"Ha ha! I'm invincible!" laughed Hiranyakashipu, "Now I will destroy Vishnu, who killed my brother Hiranyaksha!" He banned the worship of Vishnu in his kingdom. But, he was unaware of his own son worshipping Vishnu – until he found out one day!

Hiranyakashipu was furious. He shook Prahlada up and slapped him hard, "How is it that you pray to the one who killed your own uncle!" he cried.

Prahlada said calmly, "Uncle was cruel. In killing him, Lord Vishnu has only punished him for his sins."

"Do not call him Lord!" Hiranyakashipu shouted, "It is I, not him, who is the lord of the universe."

At this, Prahlada said, "There is no one greater than him, O father! He alone is the lord of the lords."

"Look here, Prahlada!" Hiranyakashipu warned the boy, "If you do not stop this nonsense, I shall severely punish you. And I may even forget that you are my son!"

But Prahlada was not afraid of his father; he continued to worship his lord as usual. "Vishnu is everywhere," he used to sing.

Hiranyakashipu tried threats, beatings, sweet words, and what not! But nothing could sway Prahlada from his steadfast devotion. Finally, the demon-king ordered his soldiers to kill Prahlada!

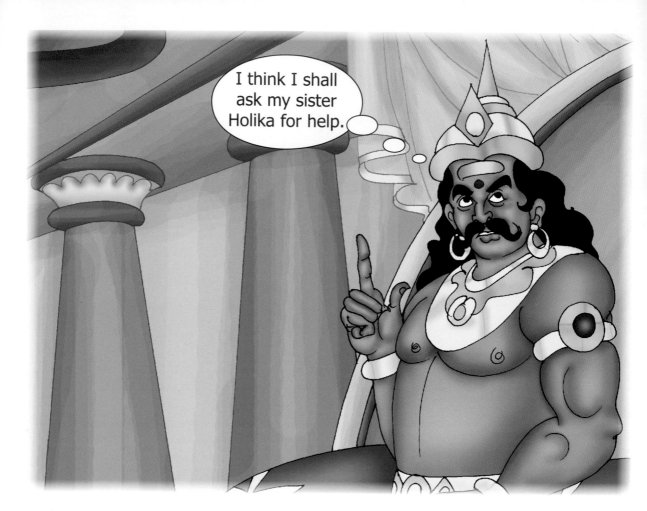

They attacked the boy as he sat meditating. But their weapons were seized in the air and could not even touch the virtuous boy. Next, the soldiers took Prahlada to the river, tied him to a heavy stone and threw him into the river. But lo! Prahlada stayed afloat! Hiranyakashipu could not believe it.

Holika, Hiranyakashipu's sister, had a boon to endure fire. So, she grabbed Prahlada and entered into a fierce, blazing fire. But surprisingly, Holika burnt to ashes while Prahlada escaped unhurt. He continued to chant Vishnu's name and sing hymns in his praise.

Hiranyakashipu listened with growing fury as the boy sang on, "Vishnu is everywhere ..."

"Is he in this pillar too?" he asked.

"Yes, he is!" replied Prahlada.

"Then let him come out of this pillar and save you! Ha ha!" laughed Hiranyakashipu and got up to attack his son.

Just then, the pillar cracked with a terrible noise and out came Vishnu in his fierce form – that of Narasimha – half man, half lion. It was evening time. Narasimha grabbed Hiranyakashipu and dragged him to the courtyard. Then, he put him on his lap and killed him with his nails and saved Prahlada.

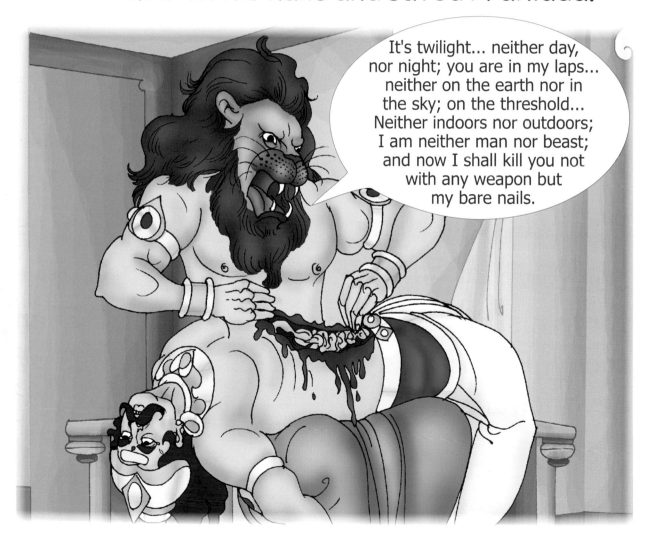

He plucked a cluster of his matted hair and created a demon from it called Virabhadra. On Shiva's command, Virabhadra created havoc in the venue of the sacrificial ceremony. He attacked Daksha and severed his head.

Shiva, too, came there to pick up Sati's half-burnt body. Carrying her remains on his shoulder, Shiva began to dance the mad dance of destruction.

Over the mountains he went dancing, the body slung on his shoulder. The ground shook and all living creatures trembled in fear. The world seemed to be coming to an end.

The Pandavas' Journey to Heaven

The great Mahabharata war was fought between the Pandavas and the Kauravas. Each side had laid a claim to the throne of Hastinapur. The Pandavas emerged victorious; it was the victory of good over evil. The eldest Kaurava prince, Duryodhana, lost his life along with all his brothers. The eldest Pandava, Yudhishthira, ascended the throne of Hastinapur.

The Pandavas ruled efficiently for many years. They depended a lot on the wise counsel of Krishna, their cousin and ally throughout the war. One day, they received the news that Krishna had left his mortal body and returned to heaven. The grieving Pandavas decided that they too would renounce this world and start heavenwards.

MEANINGS OF DIFFICULT WORDS

Satyavan and Savitri

his joy knew no bounds	– he was very happy
dissuade	– try to stop someone from doing something
steadfast	– loyal or dependable
outwitted	– was cleverer than

Prahlada

tyrant	– cruel dictator or ruler
invincible	– one who cannot be defeated
virtuous	– good, honest or trustworthy
to be an epitome of	– be a model or example of

MEANINGS OF DIFFICULT WORDS

Shiva and Sati

abode   – residence, usually of Gods or Goddesses

celestial   – heavenly or god-like

sacrificial – for surrendering or offering to be killed

frenzy   – madness

consort   – partner or wife, usually of Gods

The Pandavas' Journey to Heaven

counsel   – advice or guidance

renounce   – give up something good

caverns   – caves

unique   – one of a kind